D1451120

KAREN WEICHERT

THE JOSTEDALS-BREEN

SKALD 2008

Photos: Michael Bennett 38, Leiv Bergum 68, Breheimsenteret 20, 36, Anders Bøyum 66, Ice Troll 31, Fotoarkiv NGU i Trondheim 30, 74, Trond J. Hansen 62, Geirmund Henjum, Sogn Avis 51, Nils Kvamme 39, Finn Loftesnes 8, 29, 63, 86, Kristian Th. Loftesnes 14, Oddmund Lunde 37, Anders Aa. Mundal 69, Hotel Mundal 60a, 60b, Norsk Bremuseum 18, 67, 89, OSY 5, 10, 22, 25, 65, Frank Optun Smedegård 13, 17, 42, 46, 92, Robin Strand 72, Statkraft 52, Helge Sunde 6, 26, 32, 34, 40, 42, 56, 58, 61, 64, 70, 75, 76, 78, 80, 82, 84, 85, 91, 94, Barbra Vangsnes 48, Karen Weichert 47, 54, 57.

Illustrations and map: Knut Bjelland

Cover photos: John Price (front), Stefan Winkler (a), Karen Weichert (b), Anne Rudsengen (c)

English translation: Ary Translations S.L, Gran Canaria

Graphic design: Silje Blank / Arne Barlindhaug Ellingsen
Printed by: Kaunas

Published with the support from The Norwegian Glacier Museum and Ulltveit-Moe Climate Centre.

© SKALD AS 2008

Telephone: +47 57 65 41 55
e-mail: forlag@skald.no
www.skald.no

ISBN 978-82-7959-116-0 (norsk utgåve)
ISBN 978-82-7959-115-3 (English edition)
ISBN 978-82-7959-128-3 (Deutsche Ausgabe)

CONTENTS

Fjærland.

THE JOSTEDALSBREEN – ICE IN MOTION

One's first encounter with the glacier Jostedalsbreen can be quite unexpected. At the end of an otherwise green and fertile valley, you suddenly find one of the more than twenty tongues of this majestic plateau glacier that have been given names. Approaching the glacier front you will notice that the vegetation changes. Birches get more crooked and eventually disappear completely. Up to the glacier itself, mountain vegetation predominates; mainly lichen and moss.

With its about 487 square kilometres, the Jostedalsbreen is the largest glacier on Continental Europe, and it covers 60 kilometres from the mountain Strynefjellet in the North to Fjærland in the South. The easy access and its impressive dimensions have made the Jostedalsbreen one of the most popular tourist attractions of Norway. Seeing the glacier for the first time and walking on the ice in the company of a guide with local knowledge are experiences with nature that you will remember for the rest of your life.

WHAT IS A GLACIER?

A glacier consists of ice and snow that accumulate over a long period. A simple but very telling definition of a glacier is "ice in motion". At many places the glacier is over 500 metres thick. At a depth of more than 30 metres the glacier does not act as a rigid body any longer, but as a plastic or porridge-like mass, and the force of gravity makes the ice move slowly downwards. As it is the slope of the glacier surface and not that of the ground that determines the direction the ice will take, glaciers can also move uphill. A cubic metre of pure ice weighs about 900 kilos. Underneath and inside the glacier you find tremendous forces that crush whatever they meet on their way.

The rate of movement of the ice varies from one glacier to the other. The glacier Bøyabreen in Fjærland, which is one of the fastest, moves about

two metres a day. As ice melts continuously at the front of the glacier during summer, this motion is not easy to observe. Crevasses are often the only sign. They are produced because the rate of motion is sixteen times higher at the glacier surface than close to the bottom and at the sides of the glacier. The glacier surface also cracks when the glacier meets an obstacle like, for instance, a knoll. On the Jostedalsbreen the crevasses do not get deeper than 20 or 30 metres. Further down in the glacier the pressure is so high that these cracks are pressed together again.

Where the glacier plunges down a steep rock wall we find so-called re-generated glaciers at the bottom of the valley. Now and then tonnes of ice fall down, and a new glacier is generated from the ice-avalanche masses. The glaciers Bøyabreen and Supphellebreen belong to this category.

BEFORE ABLATION

☐ Winter snow
☒ Ice

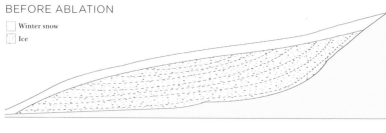

AFTER ABLATION

☐ Firn
☒ Ice

As much ablation as accumulation

Diagram showing snow and ice conditions on the glacier in spring before ablation starts, and in autumn once ablation has stopped.

HOW IS A GLACIER FORMED?

Glaciers are formed when the annual snowfall exceeds the quantity that melts in summer. Snow that has survived a summer is called firn. The firn gradually becomes glacial ice by means of a process in which small ice crystals merge into larger crystals. This is how the density of the ice increases, and that can take just five or six years on glaciers in a coastal climate whereas in the Antarctic it takes up to a thousand years. Ice is impervious to water and air. Air that remains in the ice is collected in isolated air bubbles.

On the upper part of the glacier there is usually an excess of snow in autumn accumulation. On the lower part all snow melts away during the summer ablation. At the altitude where these two zones of the glacier meet, the ablation is as large as the accumulation.

An increase or decrease of the ice masses influences the position of the glacier terminus. But as it takes a while before the ice from the upper part of the glacier reaches the terminus, it reacts with some delay. Short and steep glaciers like the Briksdalsbreen have a response duration of three or four years whereas long and gentle glaciers like the Nigardsbreen have a response duration of twenty-five to thirty years.

After the snow on the lower part of the glacier has melted in summer, we can see the blue ice. This effect occurs because the ice absorbs more of the yellow and red light than of blue light. Therefore there is more blue light left when reflected by the ice. The effect is so weak that you need large quantities of ice to bring out the blue colour.

THE GLACIER SHAPES THE LANDSCAPE

The landscape in Western Norway has been formed by glaciers over the last two or three million years. The glaciers have gradually carved out the valleys and thus formed the unique fjord landscape. The landscape has not changed much since the latest glaciation finished about 10,000 years ago.

VALLEYS AND FJORDS ARE BORN

Valleys that have been hollowed out by the glacier are usually U-shaped with steep hillsides and a relatively wide bottom. Lengthwise the valleys are often divided into several basins or troughs with separating barriers. But as the glacial rivers carry considerable sediment which thwey deposit as the water decreases its speed, today many basins are filled up and therefore not visible anymore.

It is the thickness of the glacier, the speed of the ice, and the ground below that decide how deep a glacier can carve out this shape. Where several glaciers meet, they can go exceptionally deep and form a basin. That

◁ *The sander Fåbergstølsgrandane in the valley Jostedalen*
with the glacier Stigaholtbreen in the background.

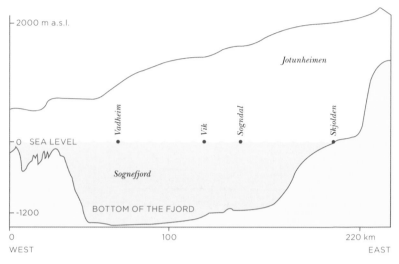

Vertical view of the Sognefjord from the mouth in the west and eastwards.

happened at many places where a tributary valley led into a main valley. Tributary valleys are often hanging valleys, i.e. the mouth of the tributary valley is situated further up the hillside of the main valley. An excellent example of this is the valley Horpedalsdalen in Fjærland, but also most of the branches of the Sognefjord are hanging valleys in relation to the fjord basin itself. The glaciers that carved out the branches of the fjords were thinner and lighter and could not hollow out the ground as deeply.

The canalisation of the ice stream also implies that the glacier can go even deeper. The valley pattern of the Sognefjord was created by rivers that carved themselves into softer areas of the mountains. This happened in a period when Western Norway was rather flat; long before the glaciations of our latest glacial era started. Later on it was the glaciers that widened and deepened these valleys. In the Sognefjord the ice probably eroded about 1,900 metres of bedrock. Seen from a bird's-eye view the Sognefjord with its many branches still looks like a river system.

Fjords are valleys that the glaciers have eroded so much that the bottom of the valley went below sea level and the ocean flowed in when the ice melted. The Sognefjord reaches 1,306 metres deep, but at the coast the bottom of the fjord has a very characteristic barrier that reaches to about 150 metres from the water surface. Here the ice masses could spread, and the glacier got thinner at its edge. As the forces of erosion of a glacier diminished according to its thickness, this thin glacier could not erode the bedrock as efficiently. Barriers could also be created because of harder bedrock that the glacier did not succeed in eroding as in the rest of the valley.

〜

ICE AND STONE - AN EFFICIENT COMBINATION

It would be impossible for a glacier of pure ice to shape a valley. But glacial ice contains particles of all sizes. They may originate from loose materials on the basal rock or from rock slides. By means of this material the glacier can model the landscape in different ways.

Owing to the weight and motion of the ice there is tremendous pressure underneath the glacier. When the ice presses a stone against the rock surface, small, curved fracture marks or scratches may be formed. If the glacier encounters an obstacle, like for instance a knoll, the pressure on the windward side may become so high that the ice melts even though the temperature is below freezing point. On the side away from the wind the pressure is minor, and the water will refreeze. As water increases its volume when it freezes, it can break up the bedrock in rifts or fissures. This is called frost weathering.

Since the glacier is moving, the pressure underneath the ice may vary a good deal. These pressure differences contribute to fracture the bedrock. A decrease of the pressure on the stationary rock may cause relief fissures that may later be a point of action for frost weathering. The loose material may freeze onto the glacier bottom or sole and will then be transported along with the ice. When it scores along the underlying rock, glacial striations are formed. Fine-grained material within a glacier has a polishing effect, just like sandpaper against a wood. Fast running meltwater carrying sand and stones also polishes the bedrock.

During these processes the stone material in the glacier sole is crushed or ground into smaller and smaller particles. Measurements from the Nigardsbreen in the valley Jostedalen show that the glacier erodes one or two centimetres off the stationary rock each year.

MORAINES – THE PASSAGE OF TIME ETCHED INTO THE LANDSCAPE

Moraines consist of unsorted loose material of all sizes deposited by the glacier. The stones in the moraines are usually rounded because of the erosion underneath and throughout the ice. Moraines that were formed along the glacier fringe are called lateral moraines and end moraines.

As the ice is constantly moving, the glacier works like a kind of conveyor belt which brings stone material to the glacier front. If the glacier moves forward, it works like a bulldozer pushing loose material in front of it, forming a large ridge. That is how end moraines are formed.

The glacier Flatbreen with a lateral moraine and an ice lake.
The cabin Flatbrehytta is right next to the moraine.

Different methods make it possible to find out when an end moraine was formed. One of most common ones is lichenometry, which determines the time-frame within which a moraine became ice-free by calculating how long it has taken for certain sorts of lichen to reach their present size. As lichen grow very slowly, this method is suitable for dating that goes back in time several thousand years, although it is more reliable for the last three hundred years.

Around the Jostedalsbreen there are marked moraines e.g. from around 1750, 1875 and 1930. At the Briksdalsbreen there is a fairly young moraine, which was formed when the glacier advanced in the 1990s.

The glacier Nigardsbreen.

The delta Bøyaøyri in Fjærland.

DELTA AND SANDER – NEW LAND IS CREATED

A large part of the stone material from glacier erosion is carried away with the meltwater from the glacier and further along with the glacial river. Particles of sand, silt and clay stay in suspension as long as the water runs fast. Stones and gravel roll along with the currents along the bottom of the river. The transport is largest in summertime when ablation is at its highest.

Where the glacial river flows into a lake or a fjord, the water calms down, and the stone material is deposited as sediments. A delta is formed where coarse materials like gravel and coarse sand remain on the shore slope whereas fine sand, silt and clay are carried further into the fjord. In this way stone material is sorted by pebble size, causing the delta to grow every year.

In summer small particles give the water a characteristic grey-green colour. These are the particles that turn the Lustrafjord and the Fjærlandsfjord green in summer. In Fjærland the rivers transport about 19,000 tons of sediments every year, which correspond to about 13 lorry-loads a day. Two kilometres outside the deltas, the fjord becomes four millimetres more shallow every year.

Where the quantity of sediments is so large that the delta builds up above sea level or water level in a lake, we get a sander. The word has its origin in Iceland and means an alluvial plain. On the sander the glacial rivers alter their courses all the time, causing the ground to be continuously changing, as well. It is rather difficult for plants to find a habitat here for a long period. The Fåbergstølsgrandane in the Jostedalen is, with its about 260 hectares, the largest active sander on the European continent.

THE LAND RISES

Today many of the postglacial deltas are situated well above sea level because of the land uplift, which took place after the ice had melted. These kinds of deltas are called terraces.

To understand why land rises, it is necessary to know how the Earth is made. The Earth's core consists of metal, mainly iron and nickel. Although the temperature at the core probably reaches up to 4,000 degrees centigrade, the inner core is solid because of the high pressure. At the outer core the pressure is minor, and it is therefore liquid. Round the Earth's core you find the mantle, and then the crust or outer layer. The Earth's mantle consists of basal rock with silicate. Conditions of pressure and temperature make the bedrock solid; nevertheless it behaves like a plastic mass. Thus you can say that the Earth's crust flows on this plastic part of the mantle, maintaining

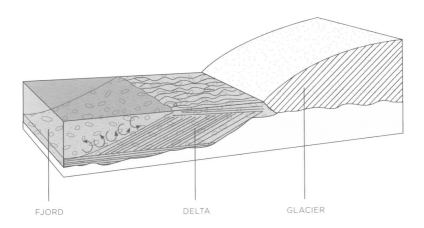

FJORD   DELTA   GLACIER

Diagram of a delta structure.

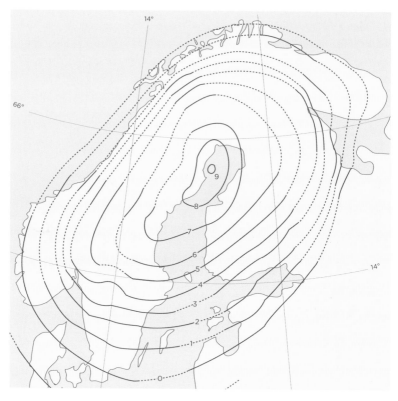

△ *Today's land uplift in millimetres per year in Scandinavia.*
▷ *The Aurlandsfjord.*

a certain equilibrium. Because of the enormous ice sheet that covered the landscape during the latest glaciation, the crust became heavier and started to sink in order to recover its equilibrium. When the ice melted, the crust was relieved, and a land uplift started. This rise was largest where the ice was thickest. The total land uplift after the last glaciation has so far been at least 300 metres, but equilibrium has still not been reached. In Western Norway the land uplift is still a few millimetres per year.

This system of equilibrium is so slow that an uplift does not start as soon as the ice is gone. But the meltwater from the glaciers led to a rise in the global sea level. The remaining glaciers caused the formation of deltas in the fjords. Due to the land uplift the river deltas were lifted up above sea level. The highest delta plain in an area marks the so-called highest coastline after the last glaciation. In Fjærland you find it at 110 metres, in the Jostedalen at 99 metres.

GLACIERS AND CLIMATE

The climate is constantly changing, as it has done since the Earth was created about 4.6 billion years ago. The most common climate till now has been so warm that ice did not exist on Earth.

Climate is the average weather during a relatively long time, whereas weather is a combination of among others temperature, solar radiation, atmospheric pressure, wind, atmospheric humidity, clouds and precipitation during a short period of time. The extreme values, like for instance highest and lowest temperature, also describe the climate.

The climate decides whether glaciers increase or decrease. Cool summers and snowy winters make glaciers thicken, whereas warm summers and winters with little snow lead to a reduction of ice masses.

Since climate and glaciers are that closely connected, glaciers become very interesting to climate researchers. By analysing the traces that the glaciers left behind and combining that data with other research methods, researchers can find out what the climate was like in the past. Following the development of the glaciers they can furthermore say something about how climate is changing in our day.

⌃ *Maximum ice extension about 20.000 years ago during the latest glaciation.*
⌄ *The glacier Austdalsbreen with the lake Austdalsvatnet.*

THE GLACIATIONS

In the history of the Earth there have been, as far as we know, five glacial periods. The shortest and most recent period is the present one, the Quaternary. This period comprises the last 2–3 million years and has been influenced by climatic fluctuations including colder periods, the glaciations, where large parts of the landmasses were covered by an up to several kilometres thick sheet of ice, and warmer periods where the glaciers had more or less melted away. Today we are in this type of a warm period.

In the Quaternary period we know of at least 40 glaciations lasting up to 100,000 years each. The warmer periods in-between usually lasted 10,000 to 15,000 years. The latest glaciation ended about 10,000 years ago.

THE LITTLE ICE AGE

More recently, the Jostedalsbreen reached its greatest extension during the so-called Little Ice Age. That was a period with a cooler climate, which started in around 1650 and lasted for 200 to 280 years. The summer temperatures were about one degree lower than today, and during this period farmers had several years of poor harvests. Winter precipitation increased, particularly in the beginning of the 18th century. Glaciers grew considerably, and for instance the Nigardsbreen advanced as much as 2.8 kilometres between 1710 and 1735. Extreme weather conditions, followed by flooding together with

The glacier Nigardsbreen in 1890 when it still covered today's glacial lake.

avalanches and slides, were not unusual. Many farms in Western Norway had their pastureland and fields seriously damaged, especially between 1680 and 1750. Between 1740 and 1750 it was at its worst. Around 1750 the tongues of the glacier also reached their largest expansion since the latest glaciation. This is evidenced by the end moraines in almost all valleys around the glacier plateau. An example is the 1748 moraine at the Nigardsbreen in the Jostedaledalen, just next to the National Park Centre Breheimsenteret.

THE EVOLUTION OF THE JOSTEDALSBREEN DURING THE LAST TWENTY YEARS

On a worldwide scale, glacial areas have shrunk considerably during the last decades. However, in Norway some glaciers close to the coast had a major surge in the 1990s. The reason was increased winter precipitation in the late 1980s and the early 1990s. In the area around the Jostedalsbreen it was the western outlets that advanced, such as for instance the Briksdalsbreen that spread 304 metres between 1987 and 1996.

This glacier expansion was very unique in a global context. Only glaciers in New Zealand and in Alaska followed a similar trend. Since the year 2000 the tongues of the Jostedalsbreen have retreated again, both in length and in volume, due to very hot summers, so now their evolution is similar to that of glaciers in the rest of the world again.

~~~

HOW OLD IS THE JOSTEDALSBREEN?

After the latest glaciation ended, there have been periods with climates both warmer and colder than today's. By analysing pollen from moors in the Joste-dalen, researchers found out that between 6,000 and 8,000 years ago summer temperatures at the Jostedalsbreen were up to four degrees centigrade higher than today. Elms, very warmth-loving trees, were growing around today's timber line for birch on the north-west side of the Jostedalsbreen. The majority or maybe all of the Jostedalsbreen had most likely melted away in that period. If that is true, the Jostedalsbreen is not one of the remains from the latest glaciation but has probably regenerated during a worsening of the climate between 6,000 and 5,500 years ago.

~~~

THE GLACIER AS A RECORD OF THE CLIMATE

A glacier is formed from stratified snow falling on the upper part of the glacier during winter. As time goes by, these layers become glacial ice. The ice therefore has the same chemical composition as the original fresh snow, as long as the ice is not exposed to ablation in summer. In this way the glacier works like a record of the climate, storing information about atmospheric composition and precipitation.

In Greenland and in the Antarctic the ice is more than seven kilometres thick. Scientists have recovered drill cores containing information about the climate from up to approximately 890,000 years back. Information about the climate in the past is very important in order to increase knowledge of the climate system and for the development of data models that are able to simulate future climate changes.

~~~

GLOBAL WARMING OR A NEW GLACIATION?

During the last 2–3 million years the warm periods between the glaciations lasted between 10,000 and 15,000 years in most cases. Should this be the case for our present warm period also, it will soon come to an end. However, many things indicate that our warm period may last a lot longer, maybe as much as another 50,000 years. The reasons are changes in the Earth's orbit around the sun; changes that recur at certain intervals.

Since the mid 1900s the average global temperature has been rising. The Intergovernmental Panel on Climate Change (IPCC) states that eleven years of the period 1995 to 2006 are among the twelve warmest years since measuring began in 1850. Heavy precipitation has become more frequent in most territories, the sea ice in the Arctic regions is melting and global sea levels are rising because of the melting of land ice.

The majority of global warming is most likely due to emissions of greenhouse gasses from human activities. The content of carbon dioxide, methane and nitrous oxide (laughing gas) in the atmosphere is now much larger than in pre-industrial times.

Today several data models give grounds for believing that the high level of greenhouse gasses can delay the natural cycle of glaciations and interglacial periods for several hundred thousand years. At this time, nobody knows for sure whether the human being has started a process that will lead to a warmer climate or whether the climate system will tend towards a new glaciation anyhow. More insight is necessary, and here glaciers are highly valuable sources of information.

◁ *The glacier Bøyabreen.*

THE JOSTEDALSBREEN NATIONAL PARK

The Jostedalsbreen National Park, with its 1,315 square kilometres ranges amongst the largest national parks in Norway and is situated in the municipalities of Balestrand, Førde, Gloppen, Jølster, Luster, Sogndal and Stryn. Almost the whole area is situated at 800 metres above sea level, and about half of it is covered with ice. Several minor glaciers that are not connected to the Jostedalsbreen, like the Jostefonni, the Grovabreen and the Myklebustbreen, are also part of the national park. The Jostedalsbreen National Park was established in 1991 and extended in 1998. Approximately 75 per cent is owned by the Norwegian State, the rest is in private hands.

A characteristic feature of the Jostedalsbreen National Park is the strong contrast between the glacier landscape in the high mountains and the luxuriant valleys with rivers, brooks and waterfalls. The preserved values are first of all bound up with the glacier itself, the glacier streams, geological formations and vegetation, but also to the cultural landscape, particularly to the mountain summer farms. The Jostedalsbreen area is, furthermore, one of the largest natural areas in Southern Norway with the so-called feature of wilderness.

The Breheimsenteret at the glacier Nigardsbreen in the valley Jostedalen.

THE NATIONAL PARK CENTRES

The Jostedalsbreen National Park today has three authorized information centres: The Jostedalsbreen National Park Centre, the Norwegian Glacier Museum in Fjærland and the Breheimsenteret in the Jostedalen.

The Jostedalsbreen National Park Centre is situated in very idyllic surroundings at the lake Oppstrynsvatnet. The buildings of the centre are meant to symbolize the encounter between past and future. The main building is a stave construction, typical building technique for houses in the Viking period. The cinema auditorium, made of polished Norwegian stone, is built in modern style. The science exhibit lays emphasis on subjects like geology, avalanches, animal life and activities on the glacier. In the cinema you can watch a film about the Jostedalsbreen. In the open-air part of the centre there is a geological park with many different kinds of Norwegian rocks. In the botanical garden, which was founded by the well-known Norwegian botanist-professor Olav Gjærevoll, there are more than 400 wild plants, most of them from the local environment. They are in full bloom from the end of May through July, but the first plants already blossom in early spring, and the last ones finish in September.

〜

FLORA AND FAUNA

The vegetation in the Jostedalsbreen National Park is greatly influenced by local climatic conditions and thus shows great variation depending on altitude above sea level, distance from the glacier and water supply. In the valleys you often find warmth-requiring diversified plant communities whereas the high mountains are dominated by alpine species. Near the glacier you find the so-called pioneer species, which are the first plants that managed to make a habitat in the poorly developed soil after the ice has melted away. Such pioneer plants are for example different kinds of lichen and moss, but also tree species like birch. Furthermore, in Norway birch forms the timber-line, which in the national park is located between 700 and 900 metres above sea level.

There is not much animal life in the high mountains and on the glacier. In the valleys there is extensive fauna with abundant deer and some rare species of birds like the white-backed woodpecker. Regarding birds of prey you find, among others, the golden eagle and the rough-legged buzzard.

⌔ *The Norwegian Glacier Museum & Ulltveit-Moe Climate Centre was designed by the architect Sverre Fehn.*

⌔ *The climate exhibit at the Norwegian Glacier Museum & Ulltveit-Moe Climate Centre in Fjærland takes visitors on a journey through time following the course of the Earth's climatic past and future.*

The Breheimsenteret in the Jostedalen symbolizes a glacier structure in the shape of two ice towers. An extensive exhibit informs about the natural and cultural history connected to the Jostedalsbreen and the area Breheimen. The centre has an auditorium where films are shown. The Jostedalen offers a wide range of nature-based activities like glacier walks, rafting, kayak trips and horse riding which are arranged through the Breheimsenteret.

The Norwegian Glacier Museum & Ulltveit-Moe Climate Centre is an interactive museum for the whole family. It imparts knowledge about glaciers and climate by means of, among other things, Ivo Caprino's panoramic film about the Jostedalsbreen, interactive models and experiments with up to a thousand year-old ice from the glacier. The interactive exhibit "Our fragile climate" takes visitors on a journey in time through the Earth's climatic history from the time the atmosphere came into being up until today and further into the future. A separate exhibit that focuses on conservation areas and outdoor life informs about the national park. The museum building was designed by the architect Sverre Fehn, who took inspiration from the glacier and the surrounding landscape, and who has won several national and international awards. The Glacier Museum also publishes an annually updated brochure about all guided glacial walks in the Jostedalsbreen area.

THE LANDSCAPE
AND THE PEOPLE

Each of the valleys around the Jostedalsbreen has its own particular history and characteristic landscape. At the same time they have a lot in common, not least because of their proximity to the glacier. The valleys and settlement sites we are going to focus on are theJostedalen, Veitastrond, Fjærland, the Oldedalen, the Lodalen and the Erdalen.

Natural conditions are very similar around the Jostedalsbreen. The bedrock consists mainly of gneiss, and the valleys are characterized by glacier rivers, which transport large quantities of meltwater down to the fjords. Many of the valleys are partly or completely filled with one or various lakes or a fjord. When the Jostedalsbreen became a tourist attraction at the end of the 19th century, the rural districts also had joint tourist activities. In many valleys tourists were brought to the glacier by boat and/or by horse and carriage.

Before the roads in the valleys and in general the modern road system of the province were ready, rural communities around the Jostedalsbreen were rather isolated. Many places you had to go by sea when travelling to and from

⊲ *The glacier Bergsetbreen in the valley Krundalen in the 1990s.*
Today the glacier has retreated considerably.

the rural districts. In winter even this communication line with the outside
world could fail. It was quite frequent that lakes and the inner parts of the
fjords froze up in winter. In some periods the ice might be too thin to walk
or drive on, and too thick for boats to get through. Then, the rural districts
were often isolated for many weeks at a time. Additionally avalanches made
it difficult to make one's way through the valleys. But even in summer the
fastest and easiest way to the neighbouring parish could be the one over the
Jostedalsbreen. This contact with the other rural communities was important, as agriculture was based mainly on self-support. With the assistance
of the neighbouring communities, households could be supplemented with

The village Flo at the lake Oppstrynsvatnet.

goods that the people on the farms could not produce themselves. In those times the Jostedalsbreen connected the rural districts. The tradition of traffic over the Jostedalsbreen dates back as far as to the 18th century, maybe even further.

Nowadays the Jostedalsbreen is somewhat a dividing line between the districts. By car you can go relatively quickly round the glacier from one rural district to the other. Traffic over the glacier is now mainly recreational. Furthermore, it is now more difficult to walk on the glacier than during the 18th and 19th century. At that time the glacier was larger, which meant a less hilly glacier with fewer crevasses.

Nigardsbreen.

⬈ *In a temporary ice cave underneath the Nigardsbreen.*

⬊ *Glacier walking on the Nigardsbreen.*

THE JOSTEDALEN – THE SCIENTISTS' FIRST GATEWAY TO THE GLACIER

Jostedalen is the name of the valley on the eastern side of the Jostedalsbreen, which stretches from the Gaupnefjord and northwards. The settlements are scattered evenly all over the main valley, including the tributary valleys Leirdalen, Vigdalen and Krundalen. The approximately 430 residents work in agriculture, industry, tourism and service trades. Many people commute to work outside the valley. The Jostedalen is today one of the most popular destinations of the province, with the glacier Nigardsbreen as the most important tourist attraction. The Fåbergstølsgrandane is today the largest active sander on the European Continent.

It was through the Jostedalen that the first scientists made their way to the glacier at the beginning of the 19th century. That is most likely the reason why the glacier eventually was named the Jostedalsbreen.

Up to the 1890s the valley was an enclosed space with no road communication to the outside world. Today there is an approximately 50 kilometre long motor road from Gaupne to the dam Styggevassdammen.

GETTING TO CHURCH ACROSS THE GLACIER

The first church in the Jostedalen, probably a stave church, was built in the 13th century and was most likely situated in settlement Jostedal just next to the present church dating from 1660. But after the Black Death the population of the Jostedalen had declined so much that the church from the Middle Ages was left to fall apart. When natural forces made it difficult to move around in the valley, it was easier for those who lived in the upper part of the valley to cross the glacier from Fåberg to the valley Erdalen and on to the church in Oppstryn. It is said that once a whole wedding procession crossed the glacier. But people might also have crossed the glacier to go to church in the Jostedalen. When young people from the valley Lodalen started out on their journey early in the morning, they arrived just in time for the service.

As the glacier was also used for those in search of a fiancée or fiancé, it

Fjærland inhabitants crossing the glacier in the 1930s.

was quite common for people from the upper part of the Jostedalen to be invited for weddings in the Erdalen or vice versa. The invitation was not binding. But if they showed up, they were often guests of honour. When wedding guests from Oppstryn came over to the Jostedalen, they were usually met at the glacier and had a welcome-drink there. Then they washed and changed to their full dress which they had brought in their sacks, and could then arrive at the farm well-groomed and in fine fettle.

THE 1959 EXPEDITION ON THE TUNSBERGDALSBREEN

With its approximately eleven kilometres, the glacier Tunsbergdalsbreen is the longest glacier arm of the Jostedalsbreen. In the 1950s the British non-profit organization "Brathay Exploration Group" was, together with several

British universities, in charge of ten expeditions to the Tunsbergdalsbreen with a total of 184 participants. One of them was John Price from the University of Nottingham. In 1959 he volunteered, only twenty years old, for an expedition which was going to measure glacier movements.

The eight-member expedition group travelled by boat via Bergen to Hermansverk and continued by lorry to the valley Krundalen. In the mountains they had to backpack all their equipment. North-east of the Tunsbergdalsbreen they set up their headquarters at about 1500 metres above sea level, one tent for cooking, and as overnight accommodation four tents, each for two people.

They mounted some weather stations, mapped out cairns and measured the velocity of the glacier. Life was simple, and so was the food. On Sundays they had tuna fish with baked beans.

Almost fifty years later, the Graduate Engineer John Price still remembers the expedition very well, among other things the sinister crevasses and the warm, sunny weather. However, the experience he remembers above all was something quite different: simply the first vista of the white glacier plains and the complete silence that reigned there.

THE NIGARDSBREEN

The Nigardsbreen is one of the largest glacier arms of the Jostedalsbreen. In 1710 the glacier front of the Nigardsbreen is said to have been situated in the middle of today's glacial lake. Some years later the glacier advanced about three kilometres and in 1743 destroyed both the houses and the cultivated fields at the farm Nigard after which the glacier was named. As the moraine ridge at the Breheimsenteret indicates the position of the glacier front in 1748 which furthermore was the largest expansion of the Nigardsbreen in recent times, the farm Nigard must have been situated somewhere between this moraine and today's glacial lake. The lake became visible again in the 1930s. The quite long and narrow Nigardsbreen reacts to fluctuations in winter precipitation with a delay of 20 to 25 years.

Since 1985, the glacier valley, the glacial lake and the lower parts of the Nigardsbreen have been conservation areas. The object of the nature reserve is to take care of a landscape of great value for research related to glaciers and botany. The reserve stretches to the 1748 moraine and today it borders on the national park. From the main road, a four kilometre long toll-road leads to the glacial lake. Alternatively you can go along a nature trail. In summer, visitors can cross the lake by the shuttle boat "Jostedalsrypa" or walk the trail along the lake to the glacier tongue.

~~

THE JOSTEDALEN FLOODED

Most people in the Jostedalen remember the 14th and 15th of August of 1979 very well, when the water level of the river Jostedøla rose incredibly fast after a period of strong ablation on the glacier due to heavy rainfall, high temperatures and strong wind. The water reached outbuildings and farmhouses and flooded parts of the road so that people had to be evacuated.

The water level finally peaked at 8.5 metres above normal winter values. Wide areas with planted fields, several bridges, a hundred farmhouses and between thirty and forty outbuildings were damaged. Farmers lost their crops, which at that time mainly consisted of hay. The main road was closed several places, so the population in the upper part of the Jostedalen depended on helicopter connections till the 21st of August. The clearing was very demanding. All the pupils from the 9th forms all over the province were sent out to help. Later it turned out that the rain had been very local. In Gaupne where the river Jostedøla has its mouth, the water level had indeed risen but the steep ground prevented damages from flooding. People did not become aware of the disaster in the Jostedalen until they saw mud and wreckage in the fjord. The last time something similar had happened in the Jostedalen was on 15th August 1898, but the flood-marks from this event are situated 1.3 metres lower than those from 1979.

HYDROELECTRICITY – THE GLACIAL RIVER AS AN ENERGY SOURCE

In the summer when it is hot, a lot of meltwater comes from the glacier, and so that is when the glacial rivers carry a lot of water compared to other rivers which have their lowest flow at this time of the year. In this way a hydroelectric power station receiving water from the glacier has a more constant power production than other types of power stations. The water is collected behind a dam and fed to the power station through tunnels. The greater the difference in height, the better. The generating station itself works like a dynamo powered by hydraulic energy.

The development of water power in the valley Leirdalen started in 1974, and in 1978 the power station started working. With a drop of 465 metres, it produces about 450 gigawatt hours, enough energy to supply 23,000 house-

holds. The power station uses meltwater from the glacier Tunsbergdalsbreen above all other sources.

The Jostedal power station in Myklemyr started production in 1989 and is mainly supplied by the lakes Kupvatnet and Styggevatnet. Through the dam Styggevassdammen the lakes Austdalsvatnet and Styggevatnet were brought together into one single reservoir. From there a 40 kilometre long tunnel goes to the turbine hall. A drop of 1,186 metres gives it the highest water pressure at a power station in Northern Europe. The production is about twice that of Leirdøla power station.

To avoid frost smoke and ice formation on the Gaupnefjord and subsequent frostbite on fruit trees, the outlet water from the power station discharges through a 15 kilometre long tunnel into the fjord 42 metres below water level.

Langedalen, Veitastrond.

The glacier Austerdalsbreen with the ice-falls Odin and Tor.

VEITASTROND – THE MOST ISOLATED PLACE IN ALL SOGN?

The about two-mile long trip along the lake Veitastrondvatnet seems endless, but the visit to Veitastrond is worth the effort. These well-run farms lie on the five-mile long alluvial plain, which stretches north-westward from the end of the lake Veitastrondvatnet. Agriculture comprises mainly milk production from cows and goats. Today about 130 persons live in this rural district which is also well-known for its production of goat cheese.

Following the toll road, you pass several mountain dairy farms where you can see livestock at pasture in summer. One of the hanging valleys, which you can see from the road, is the Snauedalen with the pass Supphelleskaret at the end. If you follow the track, you get to Fjærland and to the Sognefjord. The motor road continues all the way to Tungestølen where the valley forks. From here tracks go to the glaciers Langedalsbreen and Austdalsbreen with its three characteristic ice-falls Tor, Odin and Loke. The English mountain climber W. C. Slingsby once called it "the finest ice-scenery in Europe".

PENNED UP BY THE ICE

Before the road to Veitastrond was opened in 1956, water was the most important arterial thoroughfare. When goods like meat, cheese and butter were to be sent to Bergen for sale, they had to be delivered to Solvorn at the Lustrafjord, later to Hafslo. This was a day trip, and the goods had to be transported by rowboat and in backpacks. On their way back people brought commodities like salt and grain which were needed in their rural district. Also, mail had to be fetched at Solvorn, and before Veitastrond got its own churchyard in the 1890s, people had to carry their dead to Hafslo to be buried. In 1895 a steamer started to run regularly on the lake Veitastrondvatnet.

In winter the trip to Hafslo could be difficult. The ice was often too thin to walk or to drive on and too thick to get through by boat. This hampering ice could cut off Veitastrond from the outside world for weeks. In that case the postman often decided to go by the valley Snaudalen to Fjærland in order to fetch the mail there.

Even after the road was built, people in Veitastrond have experienced periods of up to 90 days with isolation because of avalanches. After the construction of today's tunnels, conditions have improved.

~~

THE MOUNTAIN DAIRY FARM TUNGESTØLEN

Nowadays most people attach the name "Tungestølen" to the tourist cabin that is situated 300 metres above sea level and where the valleys Langedalen and Austerdalen meet. The cabin was built in 1910 by the glacier guide Lasse Neset. From 1921 his daughter, Randi Neset, was landlady of the cabin. She was only 16 years old at that time. She cooked and took care of the tourists who came to visit, very often in connection with a hike on the glacier. At the same time she was a milkmaid at the mountain dairy farm and milked five cows and thirty goats twice a day. She also made cheese, so they were busy days, indeed. In 1965 a larger cabin was built, just next to the old one, and today it is administered by The Norwegian Trekking Association. From the cabin there is a fine view over the valley, and here the track to the Austerdalsbreen begins.

AGRICULTURE – THE GLACIER DOES THE SPADEWORK AND SETS THE BOUNDARIES

The large delta, which the glacial river has created, is quite suitable for agriculture. But preparing it required hard work. In the 19th century the alluvial plain was characterized by swamp and deciduous forest and was rather exposed to flooding. It was not until the 20th century that trenches and canals were made to drain the soil. In the early 1980s the Veitastrondvatnet was

Veitastrond.

regulated, and flood protection was built along the river.

Snow covers the meadows for up to six months a year, so it is not unusual to see two metres of snow on flat fields. Some years the farmers sprinkle "black lime" (lime with iron ore) which accelerates the melting of the snow and at the same time works as fertilizer. The climate is best suited for growing grass for winter fodder. The meadows round the courtyard houses are cut twice a year, and the grass is stored in a silo or pressed into round bales of silage.

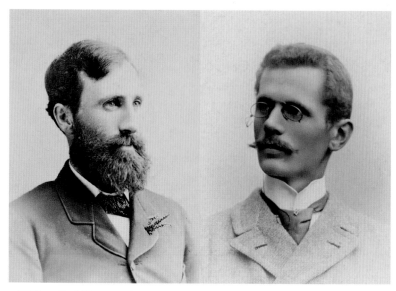

△ *William Cecil Slingsby (1849–1929) and Kristian Bing (1862–1935).*
▷ *On the glacier Austerdalsbreen towards the ice-fall Odin.*

BING, SLINGSBY AND THE AUSTERDALSBREEN

The glacier Austerdalsbreen has been a well-known tourist attraction for a long time. Nevertheless it was not until 1894 that someone set foot on this glacier: Native of Bergen, mountain climber and member of the tourist association, Kristian Bing.

On the 11th August 1894 Bing and a friend of his started the journey from Lunde in Jølster, crossed the glacier plateau and came down on the mountain ridge between the ice-falls Odin and Loke. Here they built a cairn with a white quartz rock on top of it, today called Kvitesteinsvarden. The next day they went down onto the glacier Austerdalen and via Tungestølen and the Snauedalen to Fjærland.

Chance so ordained it that another well-known mountain climber, William C. Slingsby, went for a hike on the very same day, together with a relative and the glacier guide Mikkel Mundal. From Fjærland they went over to Veitastrond where they spent the night at a mountain summer farm. Next day they arrived at the Austerdalsbreen. They went up the same mountain ridge as Bing had descended on, and continued to Briksdalen. Bing and Slingsby did not know about each other, but Slingsby realized that he was not the first man in the area when he found footprints and saw the cairn. It turned out that both Bing and Slingsby had named the three ice-falls above the Austerdalsbreen. But posterity decided to use Bing's names: the names of the Norse gods Tor, Odin and Loke.

FJÆRLAND - WHERE GLACIER AND FJORD MEET

At the end of the about 20 kilometre long Fjærlandsfjord you find Fjærland, a small rural district with its centre in Mundal. The about 300 residents are mainly engaged in agriculture, most of all milk production. The farms are larger than the average in Western Norway, and the flat ground makes them easy to run. The Norwegian Glacier Museum & Ulltveit-Moe Climate Centre is located not far from the glacier arms Bøyabreen and Supphellebreen. At the end of the fjord we find the Bøyaøyri Nature Reserve, wetlands with more than a hundred different observed species of birds and a tower for bird-watching with access for wheelchair users.

In Mundal in Fjærland we find The Norwegian Book Town which sells second-hand books in former cowsheds, the former post office and in other houses round about the village. Book towns all over the world have merged into IOB (International Organisation of Book Towns). The book town in Fjærland, founded in 1995, was the first one in Scandinavia. A good helper at the start-up was the world-famous author Jostein Gaarder. Today the book town has about 250,000 books for sale and is visited by thousands of interested customers during the summer season. All year round books are posted from this small village.

The track leading up to the cabin Flatbrehytta at 1,000 metres above sea level is one of the most popular walks up to the Jostedalsbreen. From the cabin, which is situated at only a stone's throw from the glacier Flatbreen, there is a beautiful view over parts of Fjærland and the Fjærlandsfjord.

⌂ *The cabin Flatbrehytta with the Fjærlandsfjord in the background.*
⌂ *Fjærland.*

ROADLESS UNTIL 1986

With its geographical position and the high mountains Fjærland was rather cut off from the outer world until the modern road system was built. The first steamship service on the Fjærlandsfjord was established in the 1860s. At the beginning it was a monthly service and later on ran fortnightly.

In 1892, Fjærland became part of the regular service between Bergen and the inner Sogn area, the first useable tourist route to Fjærland. Then the inhabitants of Fjærland could also receive commodities from Bergen and send milk, butter and livestock back there. In 1974 Fjærland got its ferry quay and daily ferry service. That was when it became affordable to get to Fjærland easily by car, and the supply of different commodities improved.

In 1986 the tunnel and the road northwards to Skei opened and in 1994 the road to Sogndal. Today Fjærland is situated right next to one of the central arterial roads of the province.

THE BØYABREEN AND THE SUPPHELLEBREEN

There is no other place at the Jostedalsbreen where it is as easy to reach the glacier as from Fjærland. You can go by car both to the Bøyabreen and to the Supphellebreen. Both glaciers are divided into two parts. The lower so-called regenerated glacier grows from ice masses that fall down from the upper part of the glacier. These ice-avalanches look like small waterfalls and can last up to one minute. Most of them occur during winter and spring. The moraines in the valleys Bøyadalen and Supphelledalen indicate where the ice fronts appeared during different periods. In the Bøyadalen the restaurant Brævasshytta is situated on the end moraine from 1930. The Supphellebreen is, at its 60 metres above sea level, the lowest situated glacier in the northern hemisphere south of the polar circle. In the ice-fall of the upper part, which is called the Flatbreen, the velocity of the ice has been measured at two metres a day. Each year about two million tons of ice fall down on the lower part. That corresponds to a 230-metre thick ice-sheet on a football field.

The climate in the Supphelledalen is a bit colder than elsewhere in Fjærland. In spring the snow may linger, in which case the silage harvest season starts later.

≤ The Bøyabreen in winter.

The upper part of the Bøyabreen.

AEROPLANE CRASH ON THE GLACIER

On 5th of June 1972 a single-engine aeroplane of the TA28 Piper Cherokee type with only the pilot on board was reported missing from a training flight. Three days later the wreck was found on the glacier plateau in an area where the ice moves down towards the Bøyabreen. The pilot had most likely lost control of the plane because of the fog and the well-known "white-out-effect" which makes it difficult to distinguish the sky from the ground. By means of a helicopter the pilot's body and some valuable parts of the plane were recovered, but the hull was left on the glacier and little by little covered with snow. In this way the plane was incorporated into the ice mass and probably broken into bits and pieces by the tremendous forces prevailing throughout and underneath the glacier.

In the 1990s a group of scientists hoped that parts of the plane would appear. That would give important information about the velocity and the exact direction of the ice stream. Unfortunately the airplane parts are taking a long time to come out. Maybe they have become stuck behind an obstacle on the bottom of the glacier? Or they may have come out already with one of the many ice-avalanches. In that case they are hidden in the lower part of the Bøyabreen and will sooner or later reappear.

THE JÖKULHLAUPET IN THE SUPPHELLEDALEN

The term "Jökulhlaup" is Icelandic and means glacial lake outburst flood. Such a flood can be released in different ways. At the flooding in Fjærland in 2004 the water level rose in a lake situated at a thousand metres above sea level. The lake was dammed up by the glacier Flatbreen, the upper part of the Supphellebreen, and a moraine. It overflowed and emptied down a tributary valley causing heavy damages to cultivated fields and to the road down in the Supphelledalen.

The cause of the flooding was a weather change that produced heavy ablation on the glacier Flatbreen. Water pockets and small water channels were then formed in the ice. At one time a connection opened between these and the lake, which then received an extra supply of water. That made the water level of the lake rise very fast.

On the 8th of May the water reached the edge of the lateral moraine, which consists of undifferentiated matter of all sizes. The water overflowed and started to cut its way through the moraine very quickly. The opening grew bigger and bigger each second. In just one hour many thousand cubic metres of water gushed out carrying large quantities of stone and soil down into the Supphelledalen. The road and a parking lot were covered with piles of stone. A layer of sediment up to 60 centimetres thick settled over farmland.

In the Supphelledalen a similar disaster happened in 1947, most likely also in 1920. Under the right circumstances, i.e. in periods with a poorly developed drainage system underneath the glacier, this can happen again, especially in spring or in autumn, but also in extremely mild winters.

⊰ The Hotel Mundal.

⊱ Conveyance of tourists to the Bøyabreen in the 1930s.

HOTEL MUNDAL AND THE TOURISTS

Hotel Mundal, one of the few wooden hotels that are left in Norway, was designed by the architect Peter A. Blix and has been preserved more or less like it was when it was new in 1891. It was an unusually large and expensive building at that time. The bank did not have much faith in the project and did not want to grant a loan, but the farmers in Fjærland intervened and managed to come up with funds for the builders Olaus Dahle, married to Brita Mundal, and her brothers Mikkel, Per and Johannes. In 1907 the entire loan had been repaid. The hotel is still owned by the very same family. Not only the hotel but also a large part of the furnishings from 1891 are still in use, both the imported bentwood chairs and the homemade armchairs covered in locally produced calfskin.

The guest lists of the hotel have always been full of foreign names. At the beginning, visitors usually came on their own yachts and from all parts of the world. After the First World War the hotel became very popular among American and British tourists. After Fjærland got road communication, the Norwegians also found their way to Hotel Mundal.

Most tourists came to see the glaciers. By the end of the 19th century many ships stopped at Fjærland in summer. In 1889 the farmers in Fjærland founded a conveyance company where the members had the right and the duty to present themselves with horse and carriage to give the tourists a lift from Mundal to the glaciers and back. In 1900 this cost five Norwegian Kroner, an excellent extra income for the farmers. In 1920 the first car, a Model T-Ford, came to Fjærland, and after some years it had become quite usual to use both car and horse-drawn conveyance. Today the main public road passes right next to the Bøyabreen, and several hundred thousand travellers visit this glacier every year.

THE OLDEDALEN - SURROUNDED BY GLACIERS

The valley Oldedalen on the west side of the Jostedalsbreen stretches from Olden at the Nordfjord southwards towards the glacier. From the about 1,700 metre high mountains, plateau glaciers extend their short and steep arms down into the valley which is surrounded by glaciers on almost all sides. The most well-known are the Briksdalsbreen and the Brenndalsbreen, but it is the glacier Melkevollbreen you first notice when you drive along the valley. The approximately 20 kilometre long motor road ends at the mountain lodge Briksdalsbre Fjellstove. From there a track leads to the Briksdalsbreen.

Farming is the main occupation for most of the approximately 150 residents of the valley, but tourism is also an important source of income. Some people travel to work outside the village. A major employer in the Oldedalen is Olden Brevatn AS, a mineral water producer. The drinking water comes from a reservoir underneath the glacier and may be up to 5,000 years old. The water is exported to Sweden, the US and Japan, among others.

In Oldedalen there is a wide range of outdoor activities, based on experiences with nature.

THE BRENNDALSBREEN - THE GLACIER AS A DESTRUCTIVE FORCE

The glacier Brenndalsbreen is situated in the valley Brenndalen, a hanging tributary valley of the Oldedalen. The meltwater from the glacier forms the river Brenna, which flows into the river Dalelva in the Oldedalen. During the Little Ice Age the Brenndalsbreen destroyed the farm named Tungøyane, once known as one of the best farms in the Oldedalen.

Before 1650, the Brenndalen was probably situated on the plateau of the Jostedalsbreen and not in the Brenndalen. However, during the following 50 years the glacier grew and advanced more than four kilometres. Around 1700 it reached the entrance of the valley and thus covered all the cultivated pastures in the Brenndalen. Frequent floods, ice and dirt avalanches followed this expansion, especially in conjunction with heavy rains. At Tungøyane, the home fields were gradually covered by boulders, gravel and sand. Periodically people had to abandon their houses.

In the late 1720s the harvest at the farm was so poor that farmers could not pay their taxes. In 1728 the houses were moved to a safer place. Six years

later the glacier tongue had forced its way through a small canyon just behind the place where the house had been before. The river in the valley had
changed its course and was now flowing right over the home fields of the farm.

In 1743 the glacier reached the crag just above the farmhouse. Later that
year there was a huge ice-avalanche from the glacier that destroyed all the
farm buildings, killing people and livestock. Only a twelve year-old boy and
two cows survived. The farm Tungøyane was never rebuilt.

Today you can still see the foundation walls of the houses, and at the
mouth of the Brenndalen, the moraine that the Brenndalsbreen formed
when it was at its largest. Today the ice front of the Brenndalsbreen is several
kilometres away from the farm.

THE BRIKSDALSBREEN

The glacier Briksdalsbreen at the head of the valley Briksdalen is a short and steep glacier arm that reacts quickly to climate changes. Its response time is only three to four years. When winter precipitation increased by the end of the 1980s, the glacier started to thicken. Between 1987 and 1996 the glacier front advanced 304 metres, which makes an average of up to 60 metres a year. A new moraine was formed. After some years without visible changes, the front started to retreat again, a process that became more dramatic from 2003 to 2007.

The activities on and around the glacier have depended very much on its size. The increase of the glacier in the 1990s made guided walks on the lower part of the glacier tongue possible, and an activity that soon became very

⊲ *The glacier Briksdalsbreen in 1890.*

⊳ *The waterfall Kleivafossen in the valley Briksdalen.*

popular. In 2006 the glacier tongue had diminished so much that glacier walks had to come to an end, and instead they started up guided tours by inflatable boat on the lake in front of the glacier. In addition, an activity park was built at the Briksdalsbre Fjellstove offering the opportunity for climbing and other exciting activities.

FROM FARMING TO TOURISM

At the beginning there was neither a road nor a bridge into the valley Briksdalen. The land was steep and rugged, a fact that made the farms in the valley difficult to operate. However, in the late 19th century tourists started to take interest in the glacier Briksdalsbreen.

In 1889 a bridle path was built from the farm to the glacier. The following year the road from the end of the lake Oldevatnet to the farm was finished. In 1891 farmers built a small cabin where they could sell food and drinks to the tourists who came to see the glacier. Overnight lodging was also possible. Two years later they built a hotel in Olden, steamship traffic on the Oldevatnet increased, and so did the flow of tourists.

When tourist traffic had revived after the First World War, approximately 1,200 persons were brought across the Oldevatnet each day, and from 1929 a cart road led all the way to the glacier front. At the same time goats constituted an important means of living for the farmers in the Briksdalen. They started their own cheese factory and began to sell goat cheese.

In the 1950s the restaurant in the Briksdalen was extended and the road along Oldevatnet opened. In 1966 the farmers of Briksdal closed down the farm. The goat-shed was converted into a souvenir shop and a place for overnight accommodation. The Briksdalsbre Fjellstove has become a well-established tourist enterprise.

In 1992 the deep-water berth in Olden was finished, and the traffic of cruise ships increased. By 2006, the Briksdalen welcomed about 280,000 visitors annually. The Oldedalen Transportation Company, which was founded in 1923, still carries tourists to the glacier. But after a serious accident in 2004 they decided to change from horse and carriage to purpose-built cars. Besides, these cars take more passengers and need less time for the trip.

Lovatnet.

The sheer rock wall behind the tower Skålatårnet.

THE LODALEN – BEAUTIFUL AND DRAMATIC

Lodalen is the name of the valley that stretches from Loen at the Nordfjord to the south-east towards the glacier. Most of the valley is covered by the 9.5 kilometre long lake Lovatnet. At the end of the lake, the valley trifurcates into the valleys Bødalen, Kjenndalen and Nesdalen. Only few people live in the Lodalen itself. They live mainly from agriculture and tourism. The glaciers Bødalsbreen and Kjenndalsbreen are the most important tourist attractions in the valley. From Bødal at the Lovatnet a toll road leads into the Kjenndalen, almost all the way to the glacier. At the end of the lake you find the Kjenndalsstova restaurant, which is open during the summer season. In the Bødalen a toll road leads up to a parking space at 580 metres above sea level. There is only a short walk from there to the mountain summer farm Bødalseter. The houses belonging to the farm are connected in a row which is a rather uncommon building tradition in the area. There is also a cottage for overnight lodging for members of the Norwegian Trekking Association (DNT). From the Bødalseter there is a marked path up to the Bødalsbreen. In summer you find a wide range of activities in the Lodalen, like glacier hiking, kayak trips and walks in the mountains.

THE KJENNDALEN AND THE KJENNDALSBREEN

The valley Kjenndalen has never been inhabited. There is a danger of snow avalanches at many places, particularly in spring. One of the largest avalanche is called Jørpa, or Gjørpa. The snow descends 500-600 metres from a mountain which has two different names, depending on where in the valley you are standing. In the Kjenndalen its name is Nonsnibba and in Nesdal Middagsnibba. In the narrow valley a shock-wave is generated that can be so strong that stones weighing several tonnes are moved. The forest on the other side of the valley lies pressed against the mountain side as a result of the shock-waves. The years when the Jørpa is large, the whole valley is covered with snow afterwards. If there is also wind blowing out of the valley, it may turn white with snow in Bødal, two or three kilometres away.

In the innermost part of the valley you find the Kjenndalsbreen, which many tourists came to see in summer after tourist traffic increased by the end of the 19th century. From the northern end of the Lovatnet the tourists got a lift by boat to the other end of the lake. There the farmers were waiting to bring them up to the glacier, first on horseback, later by carriage. The horses had to swim from Bødal to Nesdal to get to the meeting point. From about 1890 a steamship was used to carry the tourists across Lovatnet. The steamship "Lodalen", which started in 1902, could take 90 passengers and made several trips a day.

The Kjenndalsbreen got international publicity in 1881 after a glacier hike that W. C. Slingsby made together with the glacier guide Johannes Vigdal. They hiked from the valley Leirdalen on the east side of the Jostedalsbreen to the Lodalen. The climb down the Kjenndalsbreen was probably one of the most dangerous things this experienced mountain and glacier climber had ever participated in.

WHEN THE RAMNEFJELLET TOOK LIVES

The mountain Ramnefjellet, the almost 1,500 metre high peak at the end of the Lovatnet on the south-east side of the valley, has a special significance for the inhabitants of the valley. The name reminds them of two terrible accidents that happened in the first half of the 20th century, and which caused heavy destruction to the communities of Bødal and Nesdal. In the 19th century, those farms were considered exceptionally productive. The farmers were producing so much corn that they had a surplus to sell.

Late evening on 15th January 1905 a rock loosened 500 metres up in the Ramnefjellet, and a total of 350,000 cubic metres of stone slid down into the water. The result of this was a 40 metre high wave that crushed the buildings while the people were asleep. On its retreat, it took with it houses, people and

domestic animals. About half of the people of Lodalen died, altogether 61 persons. Only nine of them were found. The sea wave lifted up the steamship "Lodalen" 17 metres and carried it 250 metres further inland. The disaster made the area well known, and people came from all over the country to see the shipwreck. The communities of Bødal and Nesdal were rebuilt, but further away from the water.

Early in the morning of September 13, 1936 it happened again. This time even more stone slid down, and the wave reached a height of 74 metres. In Bødal all houses were destroyed. There was also heavy destruction in Nesdal and several other communities along the Lovatnet. A total of 74 persons died, 41 of them were never found. Furthermore the wave destroyed about a hundred homes and boat-houses. The shipwrecked "Lodalen" was thrown another 150 metres further inland and was dropped at 50 metres above water level. The very same autumn there were more rock slides from the Ramnefjellet, and some of them also originated huge waves, but as no people were living at the lakeshore anymore, only boats were damaged.

In 1950 the third large rock slide came from the Ramnefjellet but without causing any giant wave as the lake below the Ramnefjellet was now filled with stone material from the previous rock slides. Catastrophes like those in 1905 and 1936 are therefore impossible today, even if there should be more large rock slides. On the road between Bødal and Kjenndal a plaque with the names of all the victims has been set up in memory of the disasters.

Today there are no residents at Nesdal. At Bødal there are people living, but the houses are situated uphill from the main road that goes through the valley.

THE SKÅLATÅRNET TOWER – FROM SANATORIUM TO TOURIST CABIN

Skåla is a mountain peak at 1,843 metres above sea level in the mountain region between Oppstryn and the Lodalen. Nearby you find the tower Skålatårnet, built in stone found on the Skåla, with an inner diameter of five metres and walls more than a metre thick. The Klouman Tower, as it is also called, was meant to be a hospital for tubercular young people thought to get better in the thin mountain air. It was the outdoorsman and district medical officer Hans Henrik Gerhard Klouman who launched the project. He collected the money and organized a group of volunteers who brought additional building materials to the top. The tower was then built in the summer of 1891, and although it was not finished completely, it was already possible to spend the night there already in the autumn of the same year.

⋖ The mountain Ramnefjellet with an evident gash on its surface.

Skålatårnet.

~~~

THE LODALSKÅPA – NUNATAK AND TEMPTATION FOR MOUNTAINCLIMBERS

The Lodalskåpa is, with its 2,082 metres, one of the highest mountain peaks in Norway. What makes it different from most other mountaintops in the West Norwegian highlands is its sharp shape. This indicates that the Lodalskåpa probably rose above the ice during the ice ages. Such mountain peaks are called nunataks, from the Inuit word nunataq. For a long time the locals believed that the majestic peak was beyond their reach. The first mountain-climbers who tried their luck either ended up on the wrong mountain or had to turn back before they reached the peak. However, in 1884 three men from Nordfjord managed to do it.

Nowadays many people walk to the top of the Lodalskåpa every year. Several mountain tour associations and glacier guides' associations organize walks up there, and most of those who take the popular lengthwise-crossing of the Jostedalsbreen make a detour to the top, provided weather allows.

The following year Klouman died, and in 1896 his family gave the tower to the people in Loen who chose to pass on the responsibility to the Bergen Mountain Hiking Association. Some years later the new district medical officer Doctor Brodtkorb devoted himself to the construction of a combined bridle way and pack road up to the Skålatårnet. The road was finished in 1913. Where the road had to cross screes, they built more than a thousand steps altogether. Since those times the tower, with its 20 sleeping accommodations, has been used as a tourist cabin, even though it requires considerable maintenance and repairs because of the rough climate in the high mountains.

◁ *The glacier Kjenndalsbreen in 1997.*

The glaciers Lodalsbrekka and Erdalsbreen.

During the last decade the registered number of visitors to the Skålatårnet Tower has been between 1,000 and 1,500 per year, 60 to 70 per cent of these were guests staying overnight. Furthermore, the uphill race "Skåla opp" has increased the turnout to the tower. In 2007 the event had 1,170 contestants.

THE ERDALEN – THE MAIN ROAD ACROSS THE GLACIER

The valley Erdalen at the northeast end of the Jostedalsbreen is about 13 kilometres long and surrounded by 1,600 to 1,800 metre high mountains. The population is concentrated in the lower part of the valley. Many of the approximately 60 inhabitants engage in agriculture, although working away from the village has become quite common, too. The paved road ends at the farm Greidung. From there a toll road continues a bit further. After that, one has to continue on foot following the track that goes to the mountain summer farm Erdalssetra, which is today one of the 50 prioritised areas of cultivated landscape in Sogn and Fjordane. At the Vetledalsseter tourist cabin the valley forks into the valleys Vesledalen and Storedalen with the glaciers Vesledalsbreen and Erdalsbreen at each end.

Erdalen is a fine starting point for short trips, daytrips or the traditional tour on skis "Josten på langs". The Jostedalsbreen National Park Centre is located a few kilometres from the Erdalsbreen, on the way to Stryn.

CROSSING THE GLACIER WITH MERCHANDISE

Until the second half of the 19th century the Jostedalsbreen was maybe the most important trunk road between the rural districts around the glacier. There were many different routes. One of the most used ones was the Erdalen – Erdalsbreen – Lodalsbreen – Jostedalen. In the Jostedalen the dialect of today has a sprinkling of the Nordfjord dialect as a lot of natives from Nordfjord settled down there. People from different valleys married, they went to meetings and gatherings. Traders also used the routes across the glacier. The merchandise was often transported in backpacks.

The most important business related to the glacier traffic was cattle-droving. The increase of the population in towns and villages in Eastern Norway increased the need for meat and dairy products. In winter the cattle dealers travelled – most of them lived in Inner Sogn – to Nordfjord in order to make agreements on the purchase of cattle, horses, sheep and goats. In spring the animals were gathered at fixed places. The herding of cattle across the glacier took place in early summer before the surface acquired too many crevasses, preferably at night on hard frozen snow.

The crossing took from ten to twelve hours, but could take longer in event of bad weather. Afterwards the animals were sent up to summer pastures in the mountains. In autumn the journey continued to the market places in Eastern Norway. Later in the year the cattle dealers travelled around to get the rest of the money from those who had bought animals during the journey.

The cattle trade started in the 18th century, perhaps even earlier, and flourished till about 1910. The last cattle herd from the Erdalen to the Jostedalen took place in the 1920s.

CONCESSIONARY GUIDES

By the end of the 19th century more and more tourists wanted to take walks on or across the glacier. This generated a demand for experienced guides with knowledge of local conditions. The farmers from the rural districts around the Jostedalsbreen were very qualified for this task. In 1890 The Norwegian

Trekking Association (DNT) established the concessionary guide system. Official glacier guides were selected and supplied with map, compass and a book in which all trips had to be entered. The concession, which was valid only for certain routes, was personal and had to be renewed each year. The guides had to be available at short notice, be polite with the party of tourists and carry up to 12 kilos of luggage for the guests. In case of any serious complaint, the guide might lose his concession. There were fixed tariffs on the routes, and in 1890 the glacier guide got 12 Norwegian Kroner for the trip from the Jostedalen to the Erdalen. This was a good extra income for the farmers.

The grand days of the concessionary guides lasted till the Second World War. Now there is only one active glacier guide with a concession left, Johan Støyva from Byrkjelo. Those who want to be glacier guides today have to be authorized by the Norwegian Mountain Guide Association which was established in 1988 by initiative of the Glacier Committee of DNT.

"JOSTEN PÅ LANGS" - JOSTEDALSBREEN LENGTHWISE

Crossing the Jostedalsbreen lengthwise is considered one of the toughest skiing trips in Norway. Nevertheless, it has become very popular.

The first person who crossed the Jostedalsbreen lenghtwise on skis was probably the Fjærland native Ola Sjurson Sva, also known by the name of Ola Bøyasva. In winter 1798 or 1799 he did the about 60 kilometre long trip from Fjærland to the Erdalen in one day. Two days later he went back by the same route.

It was not until 1898 that this trip became really well known. That year the mountain climber Kristian Bing crossed the glacier on foot in three days. At the first attempt he and his travelling companions had to suspend the trip because of bad weather and an apparently insurmountable obstacle in the shape of a wind-made snow formation, today known as Bings Gryte. At the second attempt the same year Bing went from the valley Sunndalen to Fjærland together with two men from Oppstryn. They brought a large woollen blanket to sleep on at night. As they had to wade through wet snow large parts of the trip, Bing wished he had brought a pair of light skis, a piece of valuable advice for whoever were to take the trip later.

When you come down into Fjærland after the trip, you have to pass the farm Øygarden in the Supphelledalen where the glacier guide Anders Øygard lived until his death in 1993. In his old age his hobby was to ask everybody coming down from the Flatbreen what route they had hiked on. In 1992 he registered more than 800 persons having crossed the Jostedalsbreen lengthwise on skis.

FACTS

THE JOSTEDALSBREEN

Area:	487 square kilometres
Length:	60 kilometres
Maximum height:	1,957 metres above sea level (Høgste Breakulen)
Minimum height:	60 metres above sea level (the foot of the Supphellebreen)
Maximum thickness:	600 metres
Maximum measured annual snowfall:	12 metres
Glacier volume:	73 cubic kilometres
Content of fresh water:	73×10^{12} litres
	= 300 billion tubs filled with water
	= The water consumption of all Norway for a hundred years.

THE JOSTEDALSBREEN NATIONAL PARK

Established:	1991
Area:	1,310 square kilometres
Information centres:	The Jostedalsbreen National Park Centre, Oppstryn
	Norwegian Glacier Museum & Ulltveit-Moe Climate Centre, Fjærland
	Breheimsenteret, Jostedalen

FACTS OF THE MUNICIPALITIES WHOSE AREA THE JOSTEDALSBREEN COVERS:

MUNICIPALITIES	SOGNDAL	LUSTER	FØRDE	GLOPPEN	STRYN	BALESTRAND	JØLSTER
Area (km²)	746	2 707	586	1 028	1 381	430	671
Population[1]	6,822	4,884	11,465	5,723	6,706	1,399	2,928
Population per km²	9	2	20	6	5	3	4
Administrative Centre	Sogndal	Gaupne	Førde	Sandane	Stryn	Balestrand	Skei
LANDSCAPE COMPONENTS (KM²)							
Agriculture	13 (2 %)	25 (1 %)	13 (2 %)	23 (2 %)	23 (2 %)	4 (1 %)	19 (3 %)
Forest	294 (39 %)	416 (15 %)	194 (33 %)	307 (30 %)	316 (23 %)	116 (27 %)	141 (21 %)
Lakes	10 (1 %)	104 (4 %)	33 (6 %)	67 (7 %)	55 (4 %)	18 (4 %)	51 (7 %)
Other	429 (58 %)	2 162 (80 %)	347 (59 %)	631 (61 %)	987 (71 %)	291 (68 %)	461 (69 %)
CLIMATE							
Observing station	Fjærland-Skarestad	Myklemyr	Førde-Vie	Sandane	Loen	Balestrand	Skei i Jølster
Normal average temperature[2] January (°C)	-3,3	-7,1	-1,9	-0,4	-1,4	-0,6	-7,0
Normal average temperature[2] July (°C)	14,3	14,0	13,7	14,2	14,0	14,8	14,0
Rainfall[2] (mm per year)	1,905	1,350	2,100	1,260	1,075	1,370	1,760
EMPLOYMENT (%)							
In employment, 15–74 years of age	76	73	78	76	77	73	79
Unemployed	1,2	1,4	1,7	1,4	1,5	0,9	1,1
Administration	35	35	39	30	24	42	33
Private business and public service	65	65	62	70	77	58	67
Primary industries	6	10	3	12	10	4	13
Secondary industries	20	24	16	22	30	23	20
Tertiary industries	74	65	81	65	59	72	67

[1] 11.1.2007

[2] the period 1961–1990

Sources: Norsk Meteorologisk Institutt (Norwegian Weather Institute) , Statistisk sentralbyrå (Central Statistics Office) , Norsk institutt for skog og landskap (Norwegian Forest and Landscape Institute).

BIBLIOGRAPHY

Books consulted:

Bruaset, Oddgeir. 1996: *Jostedalsbreen*.

Kjærvik, Norman m.fl. 1994: *Lustrafjell. Om fjell og fjellfolk i Luster*.

Mundal, Anders Aa. 2002: *Fjærlandsfjord*.

Mundal, Anders Aa. 2006: *Jordbruk og turisme i Fjærland*.

Næss, Stein. 1989: *Jostedalsbreen og bygda den fikk navn etter*.

Nesdal, Sigurd. 1983: *Lodalen – fager og fårleg*.

Nesje, Atle. 1995: *Brelære*.

Oldedalen utviklingslag. 2003: *Oldedalen. Bygda mellom breane. Living next to the glacier*.

Rahmstorf, S. & H. J. Schellnhuber. 2007: *Der Klimawandel*.

Statens Kartverk 2003: *Jostedalsbreen. Turkart 1:100.000*.

Other information sources:
Bergens Tidende, Bjerknes Centre for Climate Research, Breheimsenteret, Briksdalsbreen Guiding AS, The Norwegian Tourist Association, Directorate for Nature Management (DN), Hotel Mundal, Intergovernmental Panel on Climate Change (IPCC), The Jostedalsbreen National Park Centre, The Norwegian Water Resources and Energy Directorate (NVE), The Norwegian Glacier Museum, The Norwegian Meteorological Institute, Olden Aktiv, Sogn Avis, Statens Naturoppsyn (Norwegian Nature Inspectorate - SNO), Statistics Norway, Statkraft, the local authorities of Stryn.

Illustrations based on:
p. 12 og 23: Atle Nesje 1995: *Brelære*.
p. 24: CICERO – Center for International Climate and Environmental Research.
p. 28: Norwegian Glacier Museum.

Special thanks to:
Per Briksdal, Anders J. Bøyum, Tom Dybwad, Sebastian Eiter, Jon Ove Hagen, Kari & Claus Kvamme, Nils Kvamme, Jon Rasmus Langeseth Vik, Audun Loen, Oddmund Løkensgard Hoel, Anders Aa. Mundal, Atle Nesje, Jon B. Nesje, Frank Optun Smedegård, Kerstin Potthoff, John Price, Anne Rudsengen, Tor Arve Sande, Christina Sogge, Trude Solli, Ingebrigd Supphellen, Randi & Ivar Supphellen, Eivind Sønstegaard, Stefan Winkler.